Alphabet of

CONSTRUCTION

This book belongs to:

_____

_____

ⓐsphalt paver

ⓑulldozer

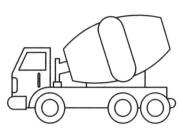

ⓒement mixer

ⓓump truck

ⓔarth drill

ⓕorklift

ⓖrader

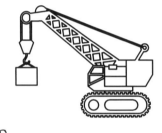

ⓗoisting crane

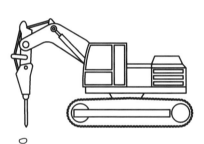

ⓘmpact hammer

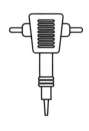

ⓙackhammer

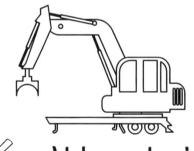

ⓚnuckleboom loader

ⓛow loader

ⓜonster dump truck

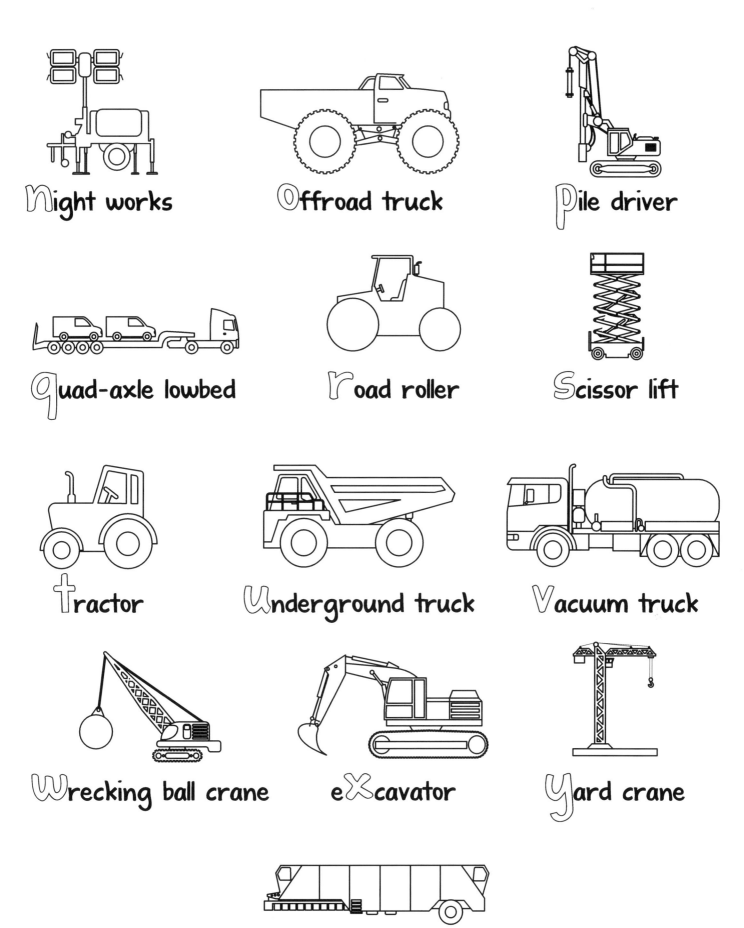

Night works

Offroad truck

Pile driver

quad-axle lowbed

road roller

Scissor lift

tractor

Underground truck

Vacuum truck

Wrecking ball crane

e**X**cavator

Yard crane

Zipper truck

asphalt paver

bulldozer

Concrete mixer truck

dump truck

earth drill

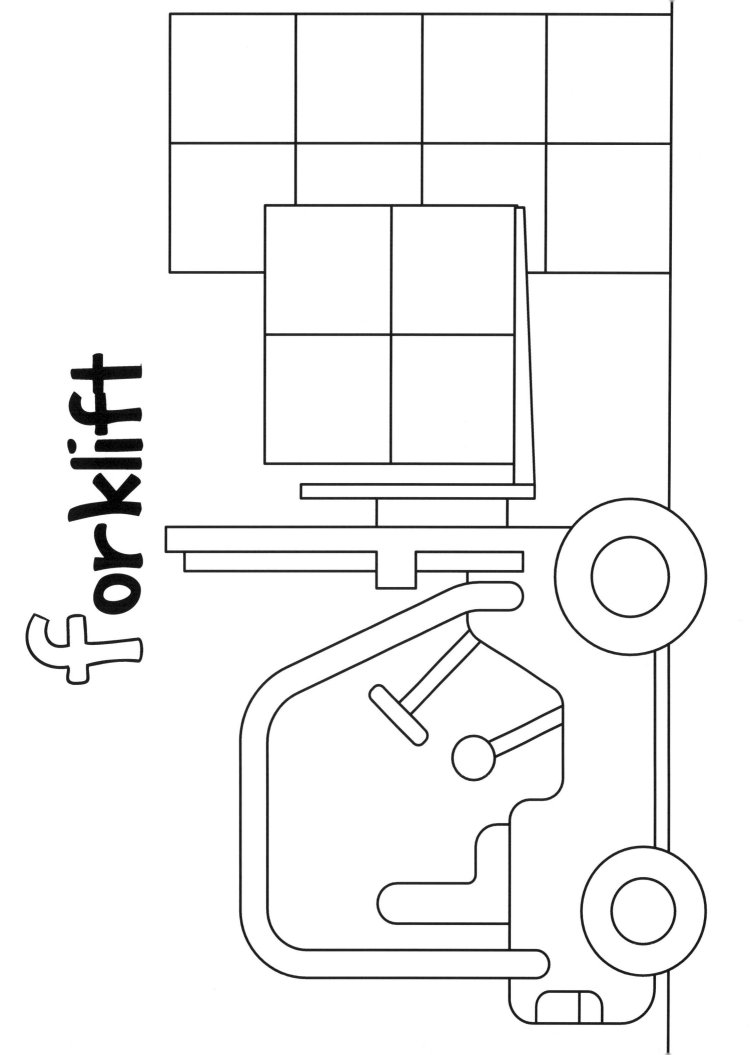

forklift

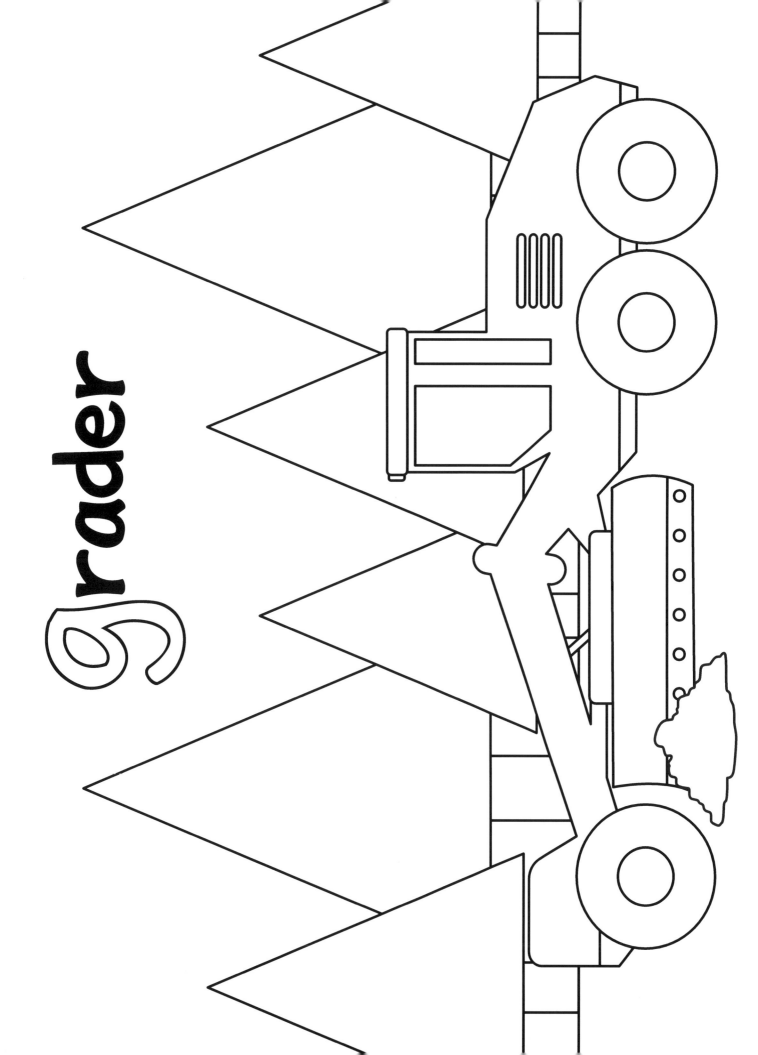

grader

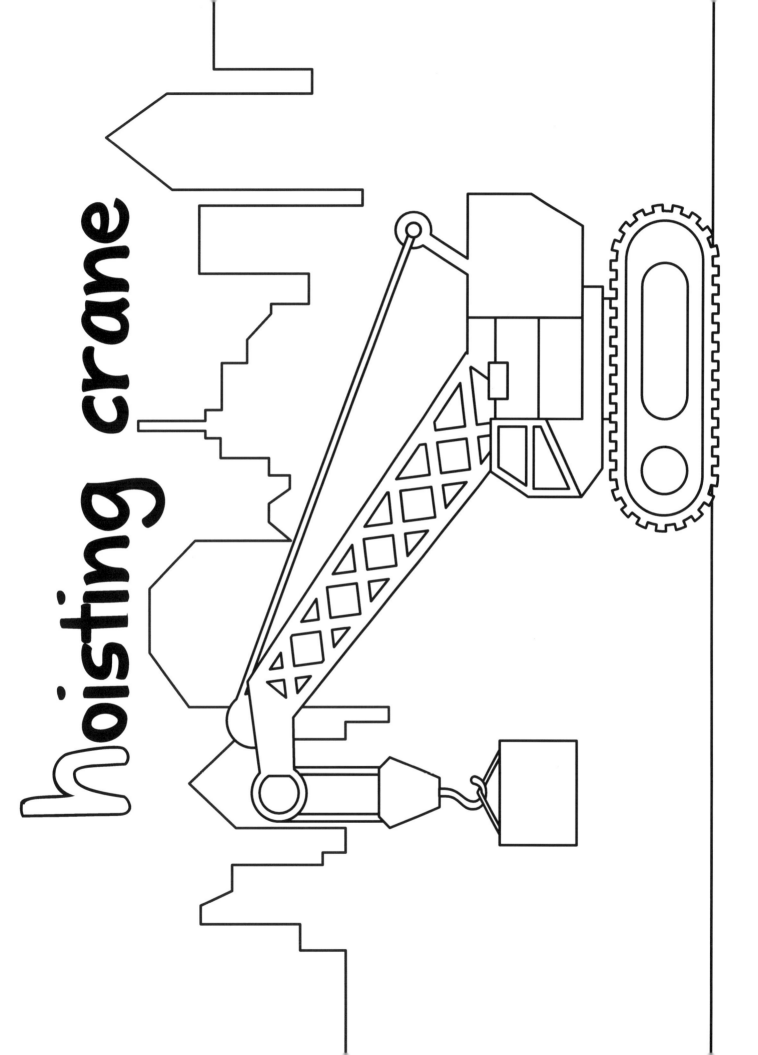

hoisting crane

Impact hammer

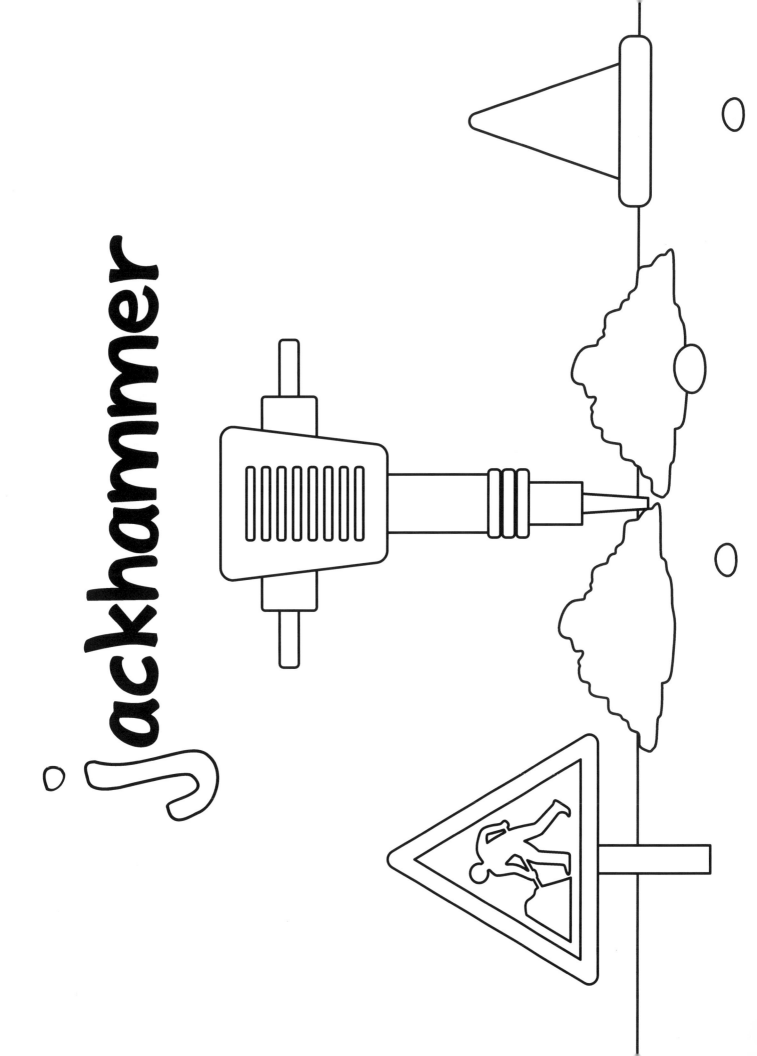

Jackhammer

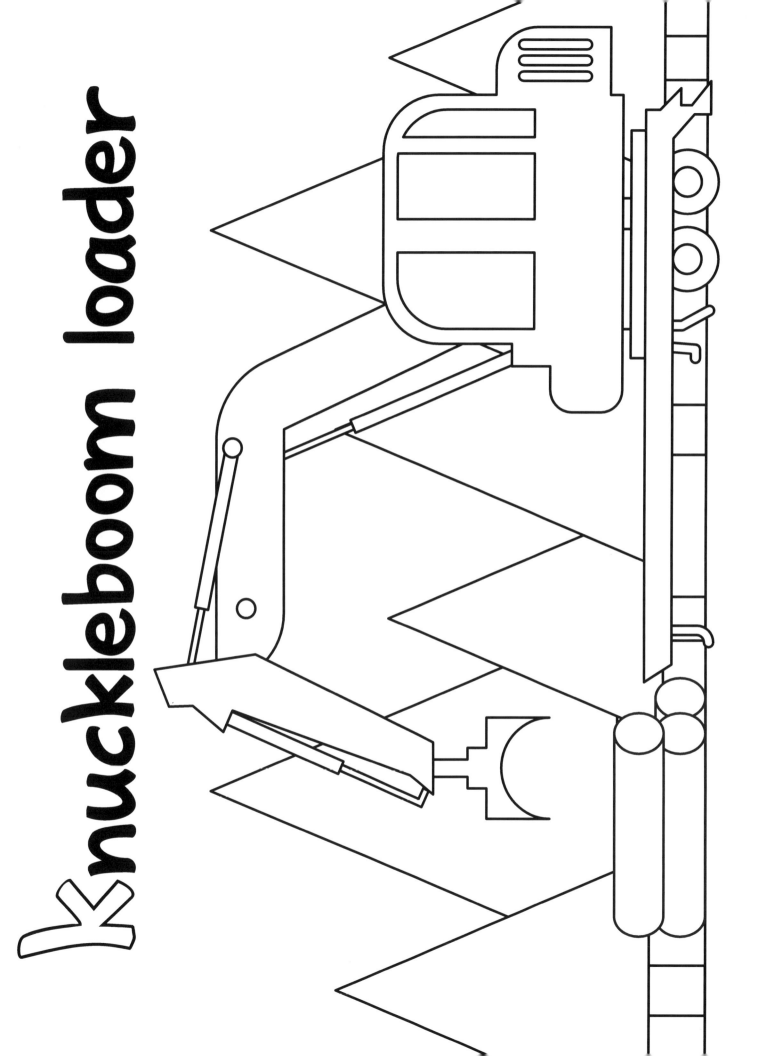

Knuckleboom loader

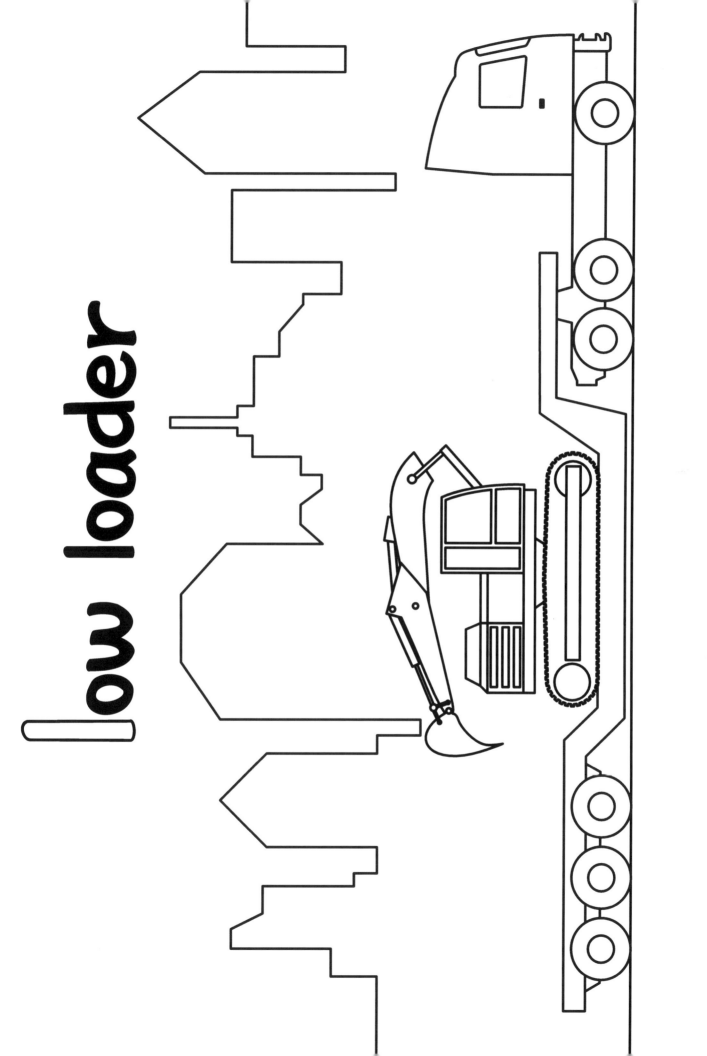

low loader

Monster dump truck

Offroad truck

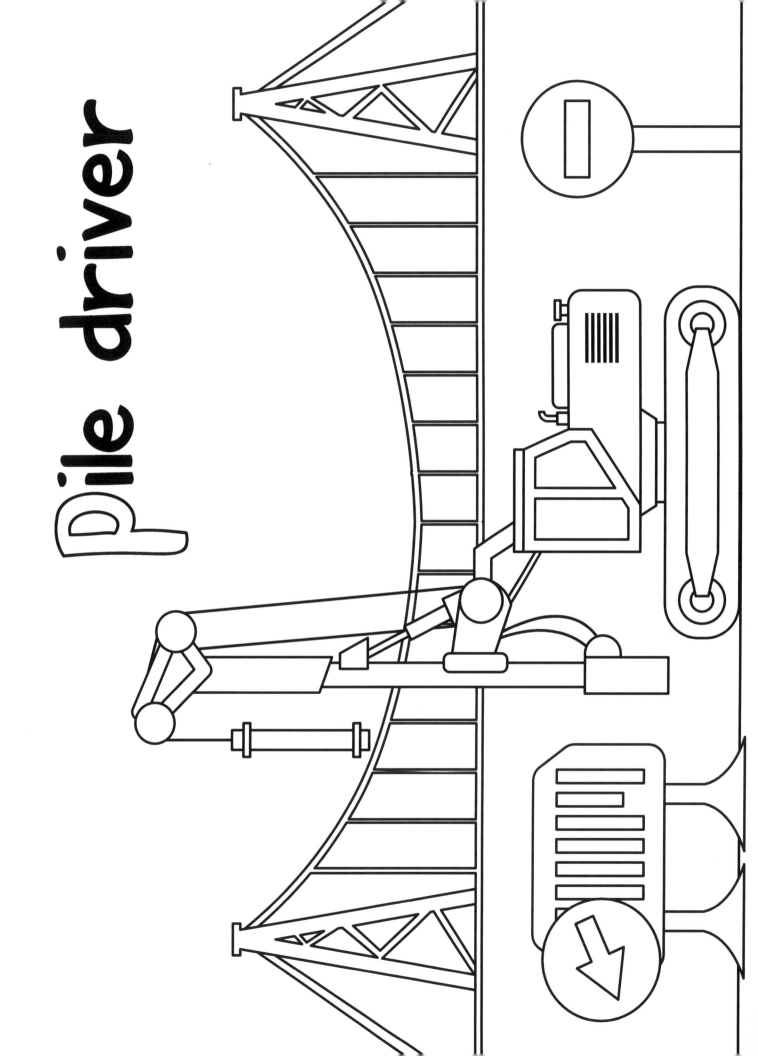

Pile driver

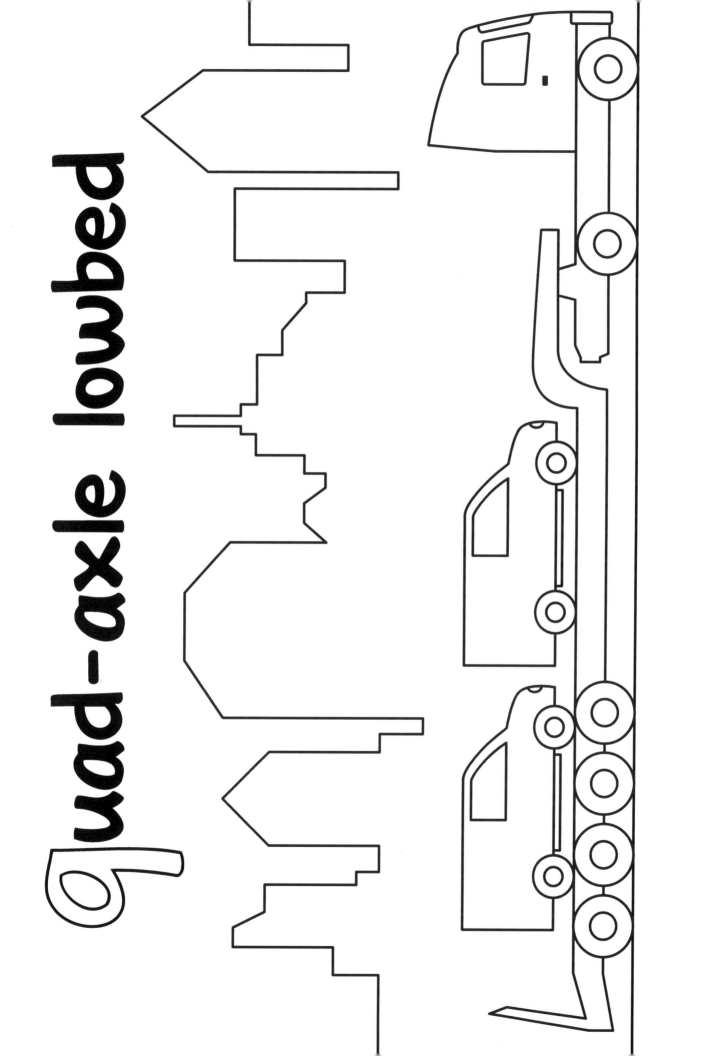

quad-axle lowbed

road roller

Scissor lift

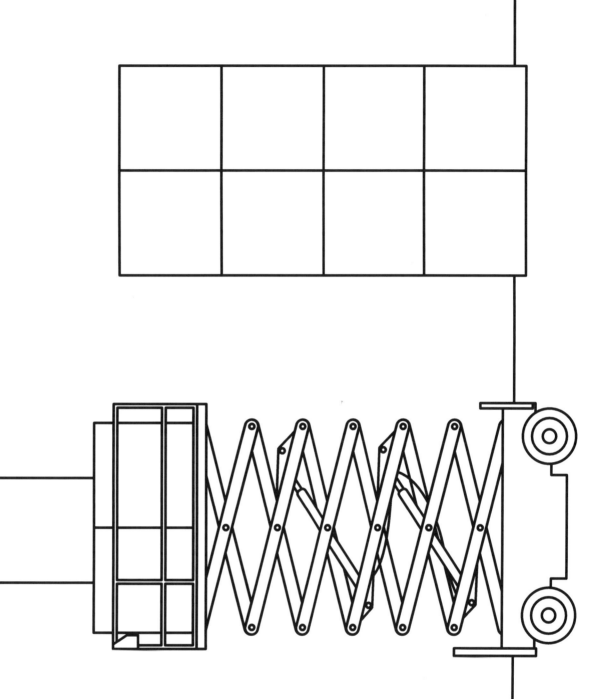

tractor

Underground truck

Vacuum truck

Wrecking ball crane

eXcavator

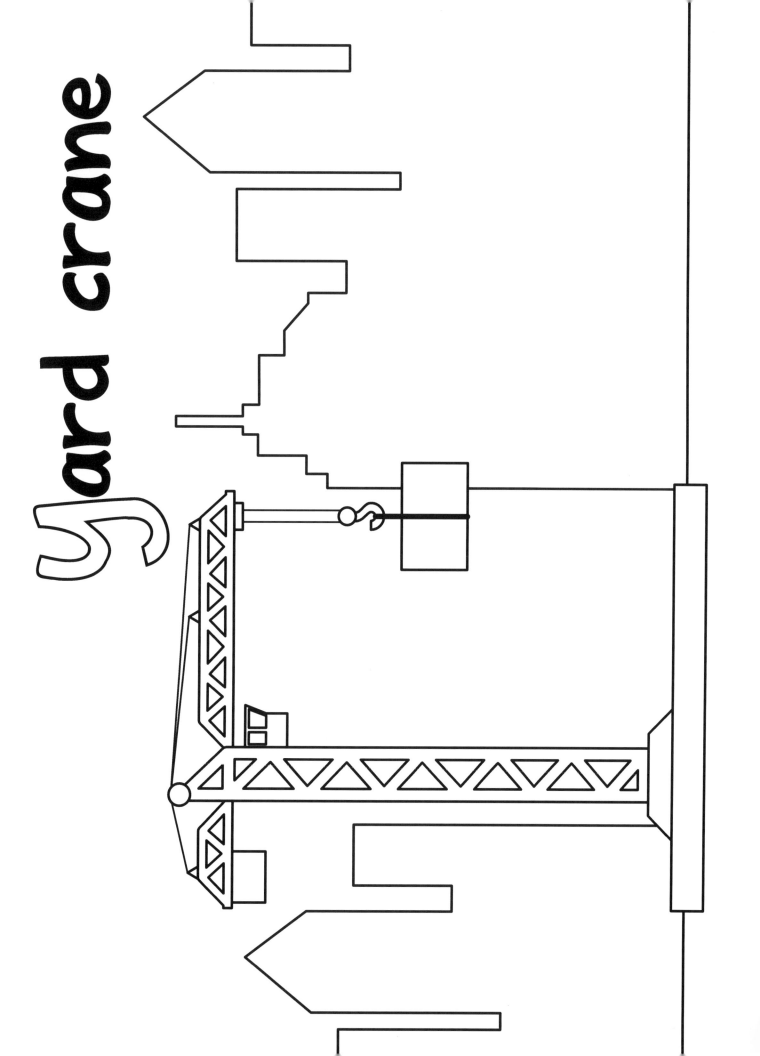

yard crane

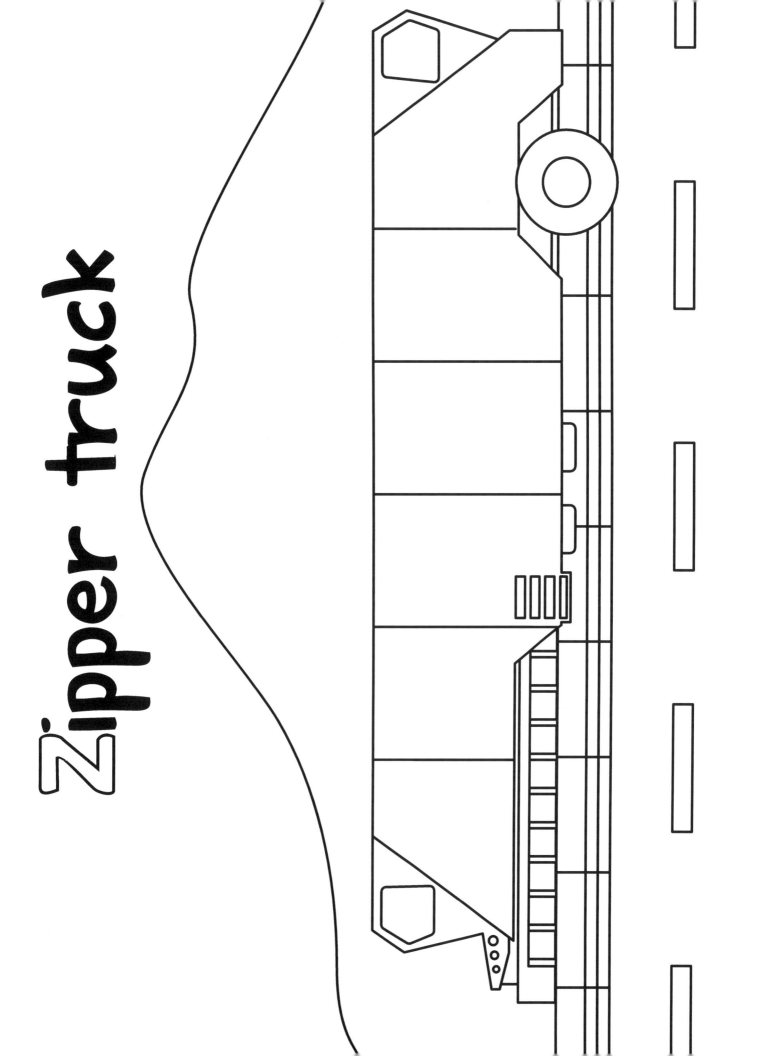

Zipper truck

A quick favour to ask.

FairyWren Publishing is a small family business and your feedback means the world to us, both personally and to help others find our books on Amazon.

In just two clicks, please leave a review (or just a star rating) by visiting:

https://fairywrenpublishers.com/review

Thank you!

FairyWren Publishing

We hope you loved the book.
The fun doesn't have to stop here...

15 bonus images to download,
print and colour in.

scan me! or visit
https://FairyWrenPublishers.com/free

Made in United States
Troutdale, OR
07/28/2024

21587086R00033